Cleaning w.

John and Marilyn Talbot

Illustrated by Mike Lacey

Nelson

Contents

Chapter I When I'm cleaning windows

Every other week, the window cleaner came to
Wellington Square.
First he started with Mr Patel, and cleaned
his shop windows.
Jamila smiled when he came round.
His name was Max.
Jamila always showed Max if he had missed
anything.
Max would pull a face, then splash some water on
the window to clean it again.
All the children thought Max was great, because he
would joke with them as he cleaned the windows.

After Mr Patel's shop, Max went to the Fish and
Chip shop and cleaned Mr Crisp's windows.
Sometimes, Max would buy a bag of chips and
eat them in the park.
Fred, who looked after the park, would come over
and they would have a little talk together.

Fred always told Max what was going on in
Wellington Square.
Max told Fred he thought the park was great.
'I would like my garden to be like this, with a lovely
statue in it,' said Max.
'You have made the park look lovely, Fred.'
Fred was pleased to hear this.
'I try hard,' he said.
'Better get back to cleaning windows,' said Max.
'See you later,' said Fred.

After the Fish and Chip shop, Max came to
the first house on his round.
This was Rocky's house.
Rocky made fun of the window cleaner because
he had the same name as his dog!
If Rocky said to his dog, 'Sit, Max!', the window
cleaner would also sit.
Rocky always laughed when he did this.

Just along the street from Rocky's house was
Number 8, where Fred lived.
Max always made sure he cleaned these windows
very carefully.
This was not because he was afraid Fred might
be watching from across the street.
He did it because Fred was his friend.

9

Then he went to the house where Wing Chan lived.
Wing Chan and his family were always pleased to
see Max.
'That Max always makes me smile. Sometimes he
talks in Chinese,' said Mr Chan.
Once Max tried to clean their windows with
chopsticks.
'Good joke,' said Mr Chan.
'Good joke, Max.'

Max went on to the next house.
Mr Keeping lived there.
Max had seen the chimp and the snake before, so
he was not at all surprised when one of the
animals came up to the window.
They always wanted to see what he was doing.
Sometimes Bruce would move his head, following
Max as he cleaned.
Sometimes Brian would try and clean the window
from the inside.
Max was really happy cleaning windows for the
people in Wellington Square.
He made lots of friends there.
Everyone in Wellington Square was upset when
they heard about his terrible accident.

11

Chapter 2 Accident!

This is what happened one day.
The windows in the house where Mrs Valentine
lived were higher than most of the others in
Wellington Square.
Max had to use a much longer ladder to
clean the upstairs windows.
Mrs Valentine did not know that Max was
cleaning her windows that day.

Max had just got to the top of the ladder when
it happened.
Mrs Valentine opened the top window to give
some food to the birds.
She did not see Max cleaning the windows.
The window hit the ladder. The ladder slipped.
'Watch out, Max!' she shouted.
She saw Max fall from the ladder.

Max was falling.
He was falling really quickly.
There was a terrible noise as he and the ladder
slammed into the ground with a loud crash.
Mrs Valentine could not believe what had
just happened.

In no time at all a number of people
came running to help.
Mr Keeping from next door saw what had happened.
He had already called for an ambulance.
He had told the ambulance men about the accident,
and they said they would come quickly.

Mrs Valentine ran downstairs.

She was out of breath and very worried.

'Is he all right?' she asked.

'I don't think so,' said Mrs Miller, who had run over to help. 'Look, there is a cut on his head,' she said.

'What have I done?' said Mrs Valentine.

The ambulance came quickly.
The ambulance men put Max into the
ambulance very carefully.
Soon he was on his way to hospital.

17

Max was hurt.
The doctor did what he could for Max, and
slowly he began to get better.
Lots of people came in to see Max.
Many people came from Wellington Square.
Mrs Valentine came every day.
She was feeling upset because she was the one
who pushed Max off the ladder.
'Don't be worried,' said Max. 'I know
it was an accident.'

Chapter 3 Bring and Buy Day

But Mrs Valentine was worried.
'Poor Max could be in hospital for a long time.
He can't clean windows, so he can't make any
money. I must do something to help.'
Mrs Valentine asked Mrs Miller if she could
think of anything.
'What can we do to help Max now he is in hospital?'
she asked.

As Fred took them home, Mrs Miller suddenly thought of something.

'We could have a Bring and Buy Day.'

'What's that?' asked Mrs Valentine.

'We all bring something we don't use any more, and we buy something we want,' said Mrs Miller.

'That sounds good,' said Mrs Valentine.

'All the money we make can go to Max,' said Mrs Miller.

'What a brilliant thought,' said Mrs Valentine.

'That sounds great!' said Fred.

So that's what they did.

First, Mrs Valentine and Mrs Miller made a poster.
It was bright red and yellow. It said,
'BRING AND BUY DAY.
Max, our window cleaner, fell from his ladder last
week and is now in hospital. We would like to
help get some money for Max and his family.
So, on Saturday, we are having a Bring and Buy
Day at Waterloo School at ten o'clock.
Please come.
Please bring something.
Please buy something.
All the money goes to Max.'
Mr Patel was very happy to put the poster
up in his shop window.

21

Soon, everyone was talking about the
Bring and Buy Day.
What should they bring?
What would they buy?
Everyone in the Square wanted to come.

At ten o'clock on Saturday morning lots of
people came to the school.
Mrs Valentine and Mrs Miller were at the
door to show everyone in.
Many of them had never been to a
Bring and Buy Day before.
They all wanted to help Max and
do what they could to make a lot of money for him.

As Mrs Valentine and Mrs Miller watched the people
go in, they were surprised.
Everyone had brought something good to be sold.
'There is no rubbish,' said Mrs Valentine.
'That's good,' said Mrs Miller.

Jamila was there with her family.
They had brought a radio to the school.
Mr Miller was there with Kevin and Rick.
They had a bike and some curtains to give away.
Tony and Tessa came with their Mum and Dad.
They had brought along a very heavy statue and
a table.
Wing Chan came along with a kite he had made.

Mr Keeping had brought a book on animals and a
strange mask with him.
Fred had a garden book to give away.
Rocky brought a football, and Mrs Valentine gave
a lovely old necklace.
'I have had this a long time,' she told Fred.
'I would like someone to buy it. I want Max to
get a lot of money today.'

25

The Bring and Buy Day went very well.
By four o'clock they had almost sold all the things.
Only the statue was left.
'It's been brilliant,' said Mrs Miller, as she put
all the money into a bag.
'It's gone so much better than I thought it
would,' said Mrs Valentine.
'I know,' said Mrs Miller. 'I haven't had so
much fun in a long time.'

Chapter 4 Max is back!

Over the next few weeks, Max got a lot better.
'You will be going home soon,' said the doctor.
'But before you go there are some people
here to see you.'

In walked Mrs Valentine, followed by all Max's
friends from Wellington Square.
'We have had a Bring and Buy Day for
you, Max,' said Mrs Valentine.
'Really?' said Max. 'What a surprise!'
'We want you to have this money,' said Fred.
At first Max did not know what to say.
At last he said, 'This is lovely of you. This is
more than I get for two months of window cleaning.'
Everyone smiled.
'I hope to be back cleaning your windows soon,'
said Max.

29

Max was soon back to doing his window cleaning.
When he got to Mrs Valentine's house, he
went in for a cup of tea.
She told Max all about the Bring and Buy Day.
'Everything was sold,' she said, 'but I do have this
statue left over.'
When Max saw the statue he was very pleased.
'That's just what I want for my garden,' he said.
'What a surprise!'

'Everyone in Wellington Square has been so good to me,' said Max.
'You have been good to us, Max,' said Mrs Valentine.
'It's great to be back!' said Max.